MY SOCCER SEASON

MY GAMES & PRACTICES

"SUCCESS IS NO ACCIDENT. IT IS HARD WORK, PERSEVERANCE, LEARNING, STUDYING, SACRIFICE AND MOST OF ALL, LOVE OF WHAT YOU ARE DOING OR LEARNING TO DO."

PELÉ,

FIFA WORLD CUP WINNER 1958, 1962, 1970
ELECTED WORLD PLAYER OF THE 20TH CENTURY

This notebook belongs to:

My Age & Age Group

My Position

My Team

My Coach's Name

My Teammates' Names

My Goals this Season

My 5 Favorites Teams

1.

2.

3.

4.

5.

My 10 Favorites Players

1.

2.

3.

4.

5.

6.

7.

8.

9.

10.

My Week

Date : _____

Week's Practice

What we worked on:

Coach's Advice to the Team:

Advice the coach gave me:

What I would like to improve:

Other sports or moments when I played soccer this week (school, friends)

Other important events this week, my goals

Match of The Week

Date : _____   Weather : _____

The Game

Opponent:

Location:

Score:

Starter/Subsitute:

Goals I scored:

My Assists:

Who scored in my team:

What the coach told me

What the coach told to the team

Our Ranking

My perception of the game, what I did well, what I can do to improve

My Week

Date : _____

Week's Practice

What we worked on:

Coach's Advice to the Team:

Advice the coach gave me:

What I would like to improve:

Other sports or moments when I played soccer this week (school, friends)

Other important events this week, my goals

Match of The Week

Date : _____ Weather : _____

The Game

Opponent:

Location:

Score:

Starter/Subsitute:

Goals I scored:

My Assists:

Who scored in my team:

What the coach told me

What the coach told to the team

Our Ranking

My perception of the game, what I did well, what I can do to improve

My Week

Date : _____

Week's Practice

What we worked on:

Coach's Advice to the Team:

Advice the coach gave me:

What I would like to improve:

Other sports or moments when I played soccer this week (school, friends)

Other important events this week, my goals

Match of The Week

Date : _____   Weather : _____

The Game

Opponent: _____

Location: _____

Score: _____

Starter/Subsitute: _____

Goals I scored: _____

My Assists: _____

Who scored in my team:

What the coach told me

What the coach told to the team

Our Ranking

My perception of the game, what I did well, what I can do to improve

My Week

Date : _____

Week's Practice

What we worked on:

Coach's Advice to the Team:

Advice the coach gave me:

What I would like to improve:

Other sports or moments when I played soccer this week (school, friends)

Other important events this week, my goals

Match of The Week

Date : _____   Weather : _____

The Game

Opponent:

Location:

Score:

Starter/Subsitute:

Goals I scored:

My Assists:

Who scored in my team:

What the coach told me

What the coach told to the team

Our Ranking

My perception of the game, what I did well, what I can do to improve

My Week

Date : _____

Week's Practice

What we worked on:

Coach's Advice to the Team:

Advice the coach gave me:

What I would like to improve:

Other sports or moments when I played soccer this week (school, friends)

Other important events this week, my goals

Match of The Week

Date : _____   Weather : _____

The Game

Opponent:

Location:

Score:

Starter/Subsitute:

Goals I scored:

My Assists:

Who scored in my team:

What the coach told me

What the coach told to the team

Our Ranking

My perception of the game, what I did well, what I can do to improve

My Week

Date : _____

Week's Practice

What we worked on:

Coach's Advice to the Team:

Advice the coach gave me:

What I would like to improve:

Other sports or moments when I played soccer this week (school, friends)

Other important events this week, my goals

Match of The Week

Date : _____   Weather : _____

The Game

Opponent:

Location:

Score:

Starter/Subsitute:

Goals I scored:

My Assists:

Who scored in my team:

What the coach told me

What the coach told to the team

Our Ranking

My perception of the game, what I did well, what I can do to improve

My Week

Date : _____

Week's Practice

What we worked on:

Coach's Advice to the Team:

Advice the coach gave me:

What I would like to improve:

Other sports or moments when I played soccer this week (school, friends)

Other important events this week, my goals

Match of The Week

Date : _____

Weather : _____

The Game

Opponent:

Location:

Score:

Starter/Subsitute:

Goals I scored:

My Assists:

Who scored in my team:

What the coach told me

What the coach told to the team

Our Ranking

My perception of the game, what I did well, what I can do to improve

My Week

Date : _____

Week's Practice

What we worked on:

Coach's Advice to the Team:

Advice the coach gave me:

What I would like to improve:

Other sports or moments when I played soccer this week (school, friends)

Other important events this week, my goals

Match of The Week

Date : _____   Weather : _____

The Game

Opponent:

Location:

Score:

Starter/Subsitute:

Goals I scored:

My Assists:

Who scored in my team:

What the coach told me

What the coach told to the team

Our Ranking

My perception of the game, what I did well, what I can do to improve

My Week

Date : _____

Week's Practice

What we worked on:

Coach's Advice to the Team:

Advice the coach gave me:

What I would like to improve:

Other sports or moments when I played soccer this week (school, friends)

Other important events this week, my goals

Match of The Week

Date : _____   Weather : _____

The Game

Opponent:

Location:

Score:

Starter/Subsitute:

Goals I scored:

My Assists:

Who scored in my team:

What the coach told me

What the coach told to the team

Our Ranking

My perception of the game, what I did well, what I can do to improve

My Week

Date : _____

Week's Practice

What we worked on:

Coach's Advice to the Team:

Advice the coach gave me:

What I would like to improve:

Other sports or moments when I played soccer this week (school, friends)

Other important events this week, my goals

Match of The Week

Date : _____   Weather : _____

The Game

Opponent:

Location:

Score:

Starter/Subsitute:

Goals I scored:

My Assists:

Who scored in my team:

What the coach told me

What the coach told to the team

Our Ranking

My perception of the game, what I did well, what I can do to improve

My Week

Date : _____

Week's Practice

What we worked on:

Coach's Advice to the Team:

Advice the coach gave me:

What I would like to improve:

Other sports or moments when I played soccer this week (school, friends)

Other important events this week, my goals

Match of The Week

Date : _____   Weather : _____

The Game

Opponent:

Location:

Score:

Starter/Subsitute:

Goals I scored:

My Assists:

Who scored in my team:

What the coach told me

What the coach told to the team

Our Ranking

My perception of the game, what I did well, what I can do to improve

My Week

Date : _____

Week's Practice

What we worked on:

Coach's Advice to the Team:

Advice the coach gave me:

What I would like to improve:

Other sports or moments when I played soccer this week (school, friends)

Other important events this week, my goals

Match of The Week

Date : _____   Weather : _____

The Game

Opponent:

Location:

Score:

Starter/Subsitute:

Goals I scored:

My Assists:

Who scored in my team:

What the coach told me

What the coach told to the team

Our Ranking

My perception of the game, what I did well, what I can do to improve

My Week

Date : _____

Week's Practice

What we worked on:

Coach's Advice to the Team:

Advice the coach gave me:

What I would like to improve:

Other sports or moments when I played soccer this week (school, friends)

Other important events this week, my goals

Match of The Week

Date : _____   Weather : _____

The Game

Opponent:

Location:

Score:

Starter/Subsitute:

Goals I scored:

My Assists:

Who scored in my team:

What the coach told me

What the coach told to the team

Our Ranking

My perception of the game, what I did well, what I can do to improve

My Week

Date : _____

Week's Practice

What we worked on:

Coach's Advice to the Team:

Advice the coach gave me:

What I would like to improve:

Other sports or moments when I played soccer this week (school, friends)

Other important events this week, my goals

Match of The Week

Date : _____   Weather : _____

The Game

Opponent:

Location:

Score:

Starter/Subsitute:

Goals I scored:

My Assists:

Who scored in my team:

What the coach told me

What the coach told to the team

Our Ranking

My perception of the game, what I did well, what I can do to improve

My Week

Date : _____

Week's Practice

What we worked on:

Coach's Advice to the Team:

Advice the coach gave me:

What I would like to improve:

Other sports or moments when I played soccer this week (school, friends)

Other important events this week, my goals

Match of The Week

Date : _____   Weather : _____

The Game

Opponent: _____

Location: _____

Score: _____

Starter/Subsitute: _____

Goals I scored: _____

My Assists: _____

Who scored in my team:

What the coach told me

What the coach told to the team

Our Ranking

My perception of the game, what I did well, what I can do to improve

My Week

Date : _____

Week's Practice

What we worked on:

Coach's Advice to the Team:

Advice the coach gave me:

What I would like to improve:

Other sports or moments when I played soccer this week (school, friends)

Other important events this week, my goals

Match of The Week

Date : _____   Weather : _____

The Game

Opponent:

Location:

Score:

Starter/Subsitute:

Goals I scored:

My Assists:

Who scored in my team:

What the coach told me

What the coach told to the team

Our Ranking

My perception of the game, what I did well, what I can do to improve

My Week

Date : _____

Week's Practice

What we worked on:

Coach's Advice to the Team:

Advice the coach gave me:

What I would like to improve:

Other sports or moments when I played soccer this week (school, friends)

Other important events this week, my goals

Match of The Week

Date : _____   Weather : _____

The Game

Opponent:

Location:

Score:

Starter/Subsitute:

Goals I scored:

My Assists:

Who scored in my team:

What the coach told me

What the coach told to the team

Our Ranking

My perception of the game, what I did well, what I can do to improve

My Week

Date : _____

Week's Practice

What we worked on:

Coach's Advice to the Team:

Advice the coach gave me:

What I would like to improve:

Other sports or moments when I played soccer this week (school, friends)

Other important events this week, my goals

Match of The Week

Date : _____   **Weather :** _____

The Game

Opponent:

Location:

Score:

Starter/Subsitute:

Goals I scored:

My Assists:

Who scored in my team:

What the coach told me

What the coach told to the team

Our Ranking

My perception of the game, what I did well, what I can do to improve

My Week

Date : _____

Week's Practice

What we worked on:

Coach's Advice to the Team:

Advice the coach gave me:

What I would like to improve:

Other sports or moments when I played soccer this week (school, friends)

Other important events this week, my goals

Match of The Week

Date : _____   Weather : _____

The Game

Opponent:

Location:

Score:

Starter/Subsitute:

Goals I scored:

My Assists:

Who scored in my team:

What the coach told me

What the coach told to the team

Our Ranking

My perception of the game, what I did well, what I can do to improve

My Week

Date : _____

Week's Practice

What we worked on:

Coach's Advice to the Team:

Advice the coach gave me:

What I would like to improve:

Other sports or moments when I played soccer this week (school, friends)

Other important events this week, my goals

Match of The Week

Date : _____   Weather : _____

The Game

Opponent: _____

Location: _____

Score: _____

Starter/Subsitute: _____

Goals I scored: _____

My Assists: _____

Who scored in my team:

_____

What the coach told me

What the coach told to the team

Our Ranking

My perception of the game, what I did well, what I can do to improve

My Week

Date : _____

Week's Practice

What we worked on:

Coach's Advice to the Team:

Advice the coach gave me:

What I would like to improve:

Other sports or moments when I played soccer this week (school, friends)

Other important events this week, my goals

Match of The Week

Date : _____ Weather : _____

The Game

Opponent:

Location:

Score:

Starter/Subsitute:

Goals I scored:

My Assists:

Who scored in my team:

What the coach told me

What the coach told to the team

Our Ranking

My perception of the game, what I did well, what I can do to improve

My Week

Date : _____

Week's Practice

What we worked on:

Coach's Advice to the Team:

Advice the coach gave me:

What I would like to improve:

Other sports or moments when I played soccer this week (school, friends)

Other important events this week, my goals

Match of The Week

Date : _____   Weather : _____

The Game

Opponent:

Location:

Score:

Starter/Subsitute:

Goals I scored:

My Assists:

Who scored in my team:

What the coach told me

What the coach told to the team

Our Ranking

My perception of the game, what I did well, what I can do to improve

My Week

Date : _____

Week's Practice

What we worked on:

Coach's Advice to the Team:

Advice the coach gave me:

What I would like to improve:

Other sports or moments when I played soccer this week (school, friends)

Other important events this week, my goals

Match of The Week

Date : _____ Weather : _____

The Game

Opponent: _____

Location: _____

Score: _____

Starter/Subsitute: _____

Goals I scored: _____

My Assists: _____

Who scored in my team:

_____

What the coach told me

What the coach told to the team

Our Ranking

My perception of the game, what I did well, what I can do to improve

My Week

Date : _____

Week's Practice

What we worked on:

Coach's Advice to the Team:

Advice the coach gave me:

What I would like to improve:

Other sports or moments when I played soccer this week (school, friends)

Other important events this week, my goals

Match of The Week

Date : _____   Weather : _____

The Game

Opponent: _____

Location: _____

Score: _____

Starter/Subsitute: _____

Goals I scored: _____

My Assists: _____

Who scored in my team:

_____

What the coach told me

_____

What the coach told to the team

_____

Our Ranking

_____

My perception of the game, what I did well, what I can do to improve

_____

My Week

Date : _____

Week's Practice

What we worked on:

Coach's Advice to the Team:

Advice the coach gave me:

What I would like to improve:

Other sports or moments when I played soccer this week (school, friends)

Other important events this week, my goals

Match of The Week

Date : _____   Weather : _____

The Game

Opponent: _____

Location: _____

Score: _____

Starter/Subsitute: _____

Goals I scored: _____

My Assists: _____

Who scored in my team:

_____

What the coach told me

_____

What the coach told to the team

_____

Our Ranking

_____

My perception of the game, what I did well, what I can do to improve

_____

My Week

Date : _____

Week's Practice

What we worked on:

Coach's Advice to the Team:

Advice the coach gave me:

What I would like to improve:

Other sports or moments when I played soccer this week (school, friends)

Other important events this week, my goals

Match of The Week

Date : _____   Weather : _____

The Game

Opponent: _____

Location: _____

Score: _____

Starter/Subsitute: _____

Goals I scored: _____

My Assists: _____

Who scored in my team:

_____

What the coach told me

_____

What the coach told to the team

_____

Our Ranking

_____

My perception of the game, what I did well, what I can do to improve

_____

My Week

Date : _____

Week's Practice

What we worked on:

Coach's Advice to the Team:

Advice the coach gave me:

What I would like to improve:

Other sports or moments when I played soccer this week (school, friends)

Other important events this week, my goals

Match of The Week

Date : _____   Weather : _____

The Game

Opponent: _____

Location: _____

Score: _____

Starter/Subsitute: _____

Goals I scored: _____

My Assists: _____

Who scored in my team:
_____

What the coach told me

What the coach told to the team

Our Ranking

My perception of the game, what I did well, what I can do to improve

My Week

Date : _____

Week's Practice

What we worked on:

Coach's Advice to the Team:

Advice the coach gave me:

What I would like to improve:

Other sports or moments when I played soccer this week (school, friends)

Other important events this week, my goals

Match of The Week

Date : _____   Weather : _____

The Game

Opponent: _____

Location: _____

Score: _____

Starter/Subsitute: _____

Goals I scored: _____

My Assists: _____

Who scored in my team:

_____

What the coach told me

What the coach told to the team

Our Ranking

My perception of the game, what I did well, what I can do to improve

My Week

Date : _____

Week's Practice

What we worked on:

Coach's Advice to the Team:

Advice the coach gave me:

What I would like to improve:

Other sports or moments when I played soccer this week (school, friends)

Other important events this week, my goals

Match of The Week

Date : _____   Weather : _____

The Game

Opponent: _____

Location: _____

Score: _____

Starter/Subsitute: _____

Goals I scored: _____

My Assists: _____

Who scored in my team:

_____

What the coach told me

_____

What the coach told to the team

_____

Our Ranking

_____

My perception of the game, what I did well, what I can do to improve

_____

My Week

Date : _____

Week's Practice

What we worked on:

Coach's Advice to the Team:

Advice the coach gave me:

What I would like to improve:

Other sports or moments when I played soccer this week (school, friends)

Other important events this week, my goals

Match of The Week

Date : _____   Weather : _____

The Game

Opponent: _____

Location: _____

Score: _____

Starter/Subsitute: _____

Goals I scored: _____

My Assists: _____

Who scored in my team:

_____

What the coach told me

What the coach told to the team

Our Ranking

My perception of the game, what I did well, what I can do to improve

My Week

Date : _____

Week's Practice

What we worked on:

Coach's Advice to the Team:

Advice the coach gave me:

What I would like to improve:

Other sports or moments when I played soccer this week (school, friends)

Other important events this week, my goals

Match of The Week

Date : _____   Weather : _____

The Game

Opponent: _____

Location: _____

Score: _____

Starter/Subsitute: _____

Goals I scored: _____

My Assists: _____

Who scored in my team:

_____

What the coach told me

What the coach told to the team

Our Ranking

My perception of the game, what I did well, what I can do to improve

My Week

Date : _____

Week's Practice

What we worked on:

Coach's Advice to the Team:

Advice the coach gave me:

What I would like to improve:

Other sports or moments when I played soccer this week (school, friends)

Other important events this week, my goals

Match of The Week

Date : _____ Weather : _____

The Game

Opponent: _____

Location: _____

Score: _____

Starter/Subsitute: _____

Goals I scored: _____

My Assists: _____

Who scored in my team:

_____

What the coach told me

What the coach told to the team

Our Ranking

My perception of the game, what I did well, what I can do to improve

My Week

Date : _____

Week's Practice

What we worked on:

Coach's Advice to the Team:

Advice the coach gave me:

What I would like to improve:

Other sports or moments when I played soccer this week (school, friends)

Other important events this week, my goals

Match of The Week

Date : _____   Weather : _____

The Game

Opponent: _____

Location: _____

Score: _____

Starter/Subsitute: _____

Goals I scored: _____

My Assists: _____

Who scored in my team:

What the coach told me

What the coach told to the team

Our Ranking

My perception of the game, what I did well, what I can do to improve

My Week

Date : _____

Week's Practice

What we worked on:

Coach's Advice to the Team:

Advice the coach gave me:

What I would like to improve:

Other sports or moments when I played soccer this week (school, friends)

Other important events this week, my goals

Match of The Week

Date : _____   Weather : _____

The Game

Opponent: _____

Location: _____

Score: _____

Starter/Subsitute: _____

Goals I scored: _____

My Assists: _____

Who scored in my team:

_____

What the coach told me

What the coach told to the team

Our Ranking

My perception of the game, what I did well, what I can do to improve

My Week

Date : _____

Week's Practice

What we worked on:

Coach's Advice to the Team:

Advice the coach gave me:

What I would like to improve:

Other sports or moments when I played soccer this week (school, friends)

Other important events this week, my goals

Match of The Week

Date : _____   Weather : _____

The Game

Opponent: _____

Location: _____

Score: _____

Starter/Subsitute: _____

Goals I scored: _____

My Assists: _____

Who scored in my team:
_____

What the coach told me

What the coach told to the team

Our Ranking

My perception of the game, what I did well, what I can do to improve

My Week

Date : _____

Week's Practice

What we worked on:

Coach's Advice to the Team:

Advice the coach gave me:

What I would like to improve:

Other sports or moments when I played soccer this week (school, friends)

Other important events this week, my goals

Match of The Week

Date : _____   Weather : _____

The Game

Opponent: _____

Location: _____

Score: _____

Starter/Subsitute: _____

Goals I scored: _____

My Assists: _____

Who scored in my team:

_____

What the coach told me

What the coach told to the team

Our Ranking

My perception of the game, what I did well, what I can do to improve

My Week

Date : _____

Week's Practice

What we worked on:

Coach's Advice to the Team:

Advice the coach gave me:

What I would like to improve:

Other sports or moments when I played soccer this week (school, friends)

Other important events this week, my goals

Match of The Week

Date : _____   Weather : _____

The Game

Opponent: _____

Location: _____

Score: _____

Starter/Subsitute: _____

Goals I scored: _____

My Assists: _____

Who scored in my team:

What the coach told me

What the coach told to the team

Our Ranking

My perception of the game, what I did well, what I can do to improve

My Week

Date : _____

Week's Practice

What we worked on:

Coach's Advice to the Team:

Advice the coach gave me:

What I would like to improve:

Other sports or moments when I played soccer this week (school, friends)

Other important events this week, my goals

Match of The Week

Date : _____ Weather : _____

The Game

Opponent: _____

Location: _____

Score: _____

Starter/Subsitute: _____

Goals I scored: _____

My Assists: _____

Who scored in my team:
_____

What the coach told me

What the coach told to the team

Our Ranking

My perception of the game, what I did well, what I can do to improve

My Week

Date : _____

What we worked on:

Coach's Advice to the Team:

Advice the coach gave me:

What I would like to improve:

Other sports or moments when I played soccer this week (school, friends)

Other important events this week, my goals

Match of The Week

Date : _____   Weather : _____

The Game

Opponent:

Location:

Score:

Starter/Subsitute:

Goals I scored:

My Assists:

Who scored in my team:

What the coach told me

What the coach told to the team

Our Ranking

My perception of the game, what I did well, what I can do to improve

My Week

Date : _____

Week's Practice

What we worked on:

Coach's Advice to the Team:

Advice the coach gave me:

What I would like to improve:

Other sports or moments when I played soccer this week (school, friends)

Other important events this week, my goals

Match of The Week

Date : _____   Weather : _____

The Game

Opponent: _____

Location: _____

Score: _____

Starter/Subsitute: _____

Goals I scored: _____

My Assists: _____

Who scored in my team:

_____

What the coach told me

_____

What the coach told to the team

_____

Our Ranking

_____

My perception of the game, what I did well, what I can do to improve

_____

My Week

Date : _____

Week's Practice

What we worked on:

Coach's Advice to the Team:

Advice the coach gave me:

What I would like to improve:

Other sports or moments when I played soccer this week (school, friends)

Other important events this week, my goals

Match of The Week

Date : _____   Weather : _____

The Game

Opponent: _____

Location: _____

Score: _____

Starter/Subsitute: _____

Goals I scored: _____

My Assists: _____

Who scored in my team:
_____

What the coach told me

What the coach told to the team

Our Ranking

My perception of the game, what I did well, what I can do to improve

My Week

Date : _____

Week's Practice

What we worked on:

Coach's Advice to the Team:

Advice the coach gave me:

What I would like to improve:

Other sports or moments when I played soccer this week (school, friends)

Other important events this week, my goals

Match of The Week

Date : _____   Weather : _____

The Game

Opponent:

Location:

Score:

Starter/Subsitute:

Goals I scored:

My Assists:

Who scored in my team:

What the coach told me

What the coach told to the team

Our Ranking

My perception of the game, what I did well, what I can do to improve

My Week

Date : _____

Week's Practice

What we worked on:

Coach's Advice to the Team:

Advice the coach gave me:

What I would like to improve:

Other sports or moments when I played soccer this week (school, friends)

Other important events this week, my goals

Match of The Week

Date : _____   Weather : _____

The Game

Opponent: _____

Location: _____

Score: _____

Starter/Subsitute: _____

Goals I scored: _____

My Assists: _____

Who scored in my team:

What the coach told me

What the coach told to the team

Our Ranking

My perception of the game, what I did well, what I can do to improve

My Week

Date : _____

What we worked on:

Coach's Advice to the Team:

Advice the coach gave me:

What I would like to improve:

Other sports or moments when I played soccer this week (school, friends)

Other important events this week, my goals

Match of The Week

Date : _____   Weather : _____

The Game

Opponent:

Location:

Score:

Starter/Subsitute:

Goals I scored:

My Assists:

Who scored in my team:

What the coach told me

What the coach told to the team

Our Ranking

My perception of the game, what I did well, what I can do to improve

My Week

Date : _____

Week's Practice

What we worked on:

Coach's Advice to the Team:

Advice the coach gave me:

What I would like to improve:

Other sports or moments when I played soccer this week (school, friends)

Other important events this week, my goals

Match of The Week

Date : _____ Weather : _____

The Game

Opponent: _____

Location: _____

Score: _____

Starter/Subsitute: _____

Goals I scored: _____

My Assists: _____

Who scored in my team:

_____

What the coach told me

What the coach told to the team

Our Ranking

My perception of the game, what I did well, what I can do to improve

My Week

Date : _____

What we worked on:

Coach's Advice to the Team:

Advice the coach gave me:

What I would like to improve:

Other sports or moments when I played soccer this week (school, friends)

Other important events this week, my goals

Match of The Week

Date : _____   Weather : _____

The Game

Opponent: _____

Location: _____

Score: _____

Starter/Subsitute: _____

Goals I scored: _____

My Assists: _____

Who scored in my team:
_____

What the coach told me

What the coach told to the team

Our Ranking

My perception of the game, what I did well, what I can do to improve

My Week

Date : _____

Week's Practice

What we worked on:

Coach's Advice to the Team:

Advice the coach gave me:

What I would like to improve:

Other sports or moments when I played soccer this week (school, friends)

Other important events this week, my goals

Match of The Week

Date : _____   Weather : _____

The Game

Opponent: _____

Location: _____

Score: _____

Starter/Subsitute: _____

Goals I scored: _____

My Assists: _____

Who scored in my team:

_____

What the coach told me

What the coach told to the team

Our Ranking

My perception of the game, what I did well, what I can do to improve

My Week

Date : _____

Week's Practice

What we worked on:

Coach's Advice to the Team:

Advice the coach gave me:

What I would like to improve:

Other sports or moments when I played soccer this week (school, friends)

Other important events this week, my goals

Match of The Week

Date : _____   Weather : _____

The Game

Opponent: _____

Location: _____

Score: _____

Starter/Subsitute: _____

Goals I scored: _____

My Assists: _____

Who scored in my team:

_____

What the coach told me

What the coach told to the team

Our Ranking

My perception of the game, what I did well, what I can do to improve

My Week

Date : _____

Week's Practice

What we worked on:

Coach's Advice to the Team:

Advice the coach gave me:

What I would like to improve:

Other sports or moments when I played soccer this week (school, friends)

Other important events this week, my goals

Match of The Week

Date : _____   Weather : _____

The Game

Opponent: _____

Location: _____

Score: _____

Starter/Subsitute: _____

Goals I scored: _____

My Assists: _____

Who scored in my team:
_____

What the coach told me

What the coach told to the team

Our Ranking

My perception of the game, what I did well, what I can do to improve

My Week

Date : _____

Week's Practice

What we worked on:

Coach's Advice to the Team:

Advice the coach gave me:

What I would like to improve:

Other sports or moments when I played soccer this week (school, friends)

Other important events this week, my goals

Match of The Week

Date : _____   Weather : _____

The Game

Opponent:

Location:

Score:

Starter/Subsitute:

Goals I scored:

My Assists:

Who scored in my team:

What the coach told me

What the coach told to the team

Our Ranking

My perception of the game, what I did well, what I can do to improve

My Week

Date : _____

Week's Practice

What we worked on:

Coach's Advice to the Team:

Advice the coach gave me:

What I would like to improve:

Other sports or moments when I played soccer this week (school, friends)

Other important events this week, my goals

Match of The Week

Date : _____   Weather : _____

The Game

Opponent: _____

Location: _____

Score: _____

Starter/Subsitute: _____

Goals I scored: _____

My Assists: _____

Who scored in my team:

What the coach told me

What the coach told to the team

Our Ranking

My perception of the game, what I did well, what I can do to improve

My Week

Date : _____

Week's Practice

What we worked on:

Coach's Advice to the Team:

Advice the coach gave me:

What I would like to improve:

Other sports or moments when I played soccer this week (school, friends)

Other important events this week, my goals

Match of The Week

Date : _____   Weather : _____

The Game

Opponent: _____

Location: _____

Score: _____

Starter/Subsitute: _____

Goals I scored: _____

My Assists: _____

Who scored in my team:

What the coach told me

What the coach told to the team

Our Ranking

My perception of the game, what I did well, what I can do to improve

Made in United States
North Haven, CT
05 June 2023

37351265R00059